Struik Pocket Guides
for Southern Africa

Spiders

Gerry Newlands

Department of Entomology
University of Pretoria

S0-BDP-092

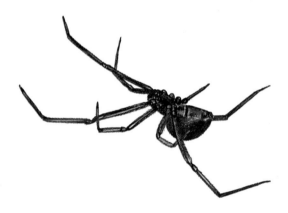

ILLUSTRATED BY
Elbie de Meillon

STRUIK

Contents

Struik Publishers (Pty) Ltd
(a member of The Struik Publishing Group (Pty) Ltd)
Cornelis Struik House
80 McKenzie Street
Cape Town 8001

Reg. No.: 54/00965/07

First published in 1986
Second edition 1995
Second impression 1997

Copyright © in text G Newlands 1986, 1995
Copyright © in illustrations E de Meillon 1986, 1995
Copyright © in published edition Struik Publishers (Pty) Ltd 1986, 1995

Set by McManus Bros (Pty) Ltd, Cape Town
Reproduction by Hirt & Carter (Pty) Ltd, Cape Town
Printing and binding by National Book Printers, Drukkery Street
Goodwood, Western Cape

ISBN 1-86825-844-0

How to use this book

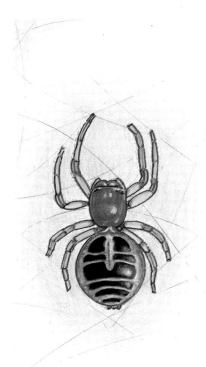

This book is not intended as a taxonomic field guide to the spiders of southern Africa, but rather as an introduction to those spiders which are very common, interesting or dangerous. The descriptions and illustrations should enable the reader to recognize the species dealt with when they are encountered.

The majority of spiders are very small and this makes their distinctive characteristics difficult if not impossible to see with the unaided eye. A 10x pocket loupe will be indispensable if you do not have a dissecting microscope.

Dorsal view of Camaricus *sp. (Thomisidae)*

To observe the species mentioned in this book, you will need to develop an awareness of webs. Many spiders are not easy to see in their webs and some species, such as the widow spiders, leave the retreat areas of their webs only at night. Species that are not web-bound are found on plants, beneath rocks or bark, or in holes in the ground. 💀

Spiders marked with a skull and crossbones (💀) are considered dangerous and should be treated with considerable respect. All spiders may bite if provoked and while the majority are regarded as harmless, their bites may be painful.

The Afrikaans name is given at the end of each account.

Legends:
♀ = female
♂ = male

3

Structure and function

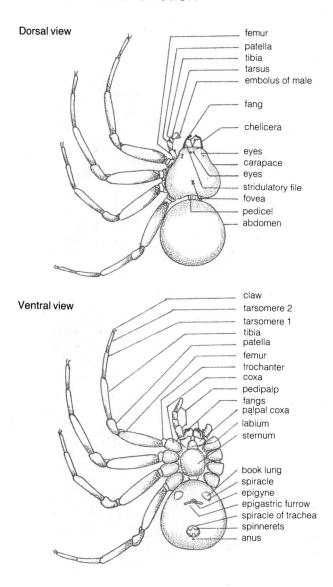

Dorsal view

- femur
- patella
- tibia
- tarsus
- embolus of male
- fang
- chelicera
- eyes
- carapace
- eyes
- stridulatory file
- fovea
- pedicel
- abdomen

Ventral view

- claw
- tarsomere 2
- tarsomere 1
- tibia
- patella
- femur
- trochanter
- coxa
- pedipalp
- fangs
- palpal coxa
- labium
- sternum
- book lung
- spiracle
- epigyne
- epigastric furrow
- spiracle of trachea
- spinnerets
- anus

Internal organs

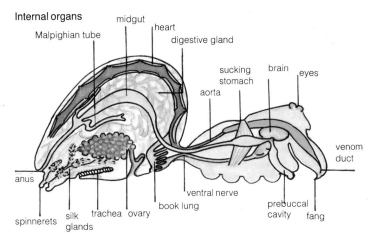

Like all other arthropods, the spider's body is contained in a fairly rigid, segmented exterior skeleton, the components of which are held together by flexible membranes. The body is composed of two body regions or tagmata: the head region (prosoma) and the abdomen (opisthosoma). The head region bears all the appendages associated with movement and feeding, namely two chelicerae, two pedipalps and eight legs. The spinnerets which spin the silk are the only obvious abdominal appendages.

Internal organs of the head region are: 1) the brain, out of which nerves branch to the chelicerae, pedipalps, legs, eyes and abdomen; 2) venom glands; 3) salivary and other glands and their muscles; 4) feeding organs such as the prebuccal cavity, mouth, oesophagus and sucking stomach; and 5) muscles which operate the sucking stomach, chelicerae, pedipalps and legs.

The abdomen contains the organs of digestion (mid-gut and digestive caeca), the heart, lungs, silk glands, genitalia and the organs of excretion (Malpighian tubes and rectum).

The feeding organs function as follows: chelicerae are used to inject venom and immobilize the prey. In some cases they are also used to chew the prey and mix it with the digestive secretions. The food is thus digested before it reaches the mouth and is then sucked up through the prebuccal cavity which is a filtering chamber to ensure that only digested liquids are imbibed. Undigested particles are filtered off. The sucking stomach provides the suction. The food then passes into the mid-gut where absorption takes place. Food reserves are stored in the digestive caeca. Nutrients are transported to the organs by the haemolymph (blood), and the Malpighian tubes remove metabolic waste from the blood. Waste is excreted through the hind-gut. Book lungs aerate the blood which is then used to transport the oxygen. Spiders (like insects) have an open blood system and the heart simply serves to move the blood through the body cavity.

Spider relatives

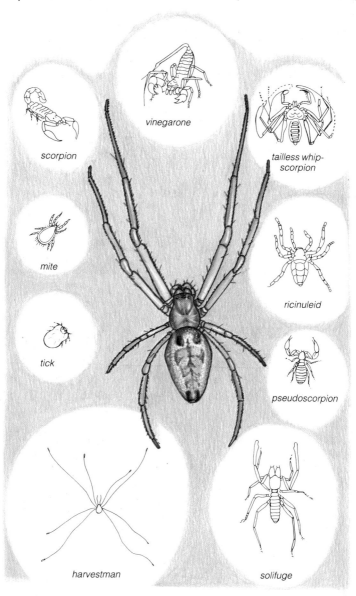

scorpion

vinegarone

tailless whip-
scorpion

mite

ricinuleid

tick

pseudoscorpion

harvestman

solifuge

Spiders represent one of many orders in the class Arachnida. All of these orders are related and the following are some of the spiders' best-known relatives.

Scorpions (Order Scorpiones). These greatly feared creatures are often called living fossils because their fossil record can be traced back at least 400 million years. They are characterized by crab-like pincers and a tail-like post-abdomen which bears the venom vesicle and stinger. Some species are lethally toxic and their venoms have a neurotoxic effect. Scorpions are widespread throughout Africa and range in size from 6 to 210 mm.

Vinegarones (Order Uropygi). Vinegarones are also known as whip-scorpions. They resemble scorpions but differ in that they have a many-segmented, whip-like tail without a stinger. When disturbed, vinegarones can squirt a powerful irritant to disperse adversaries. They are tropical creatures and measure up to 65 mm.

Tailless whip-scorpions (Order Amblypygi). Tailless whip-scorpions resemble vinegarones but lack the tail. Instead, they have greatly lengthened front legs which are modified to form whip-like tactile organs. These creatures are quite harmless in spite of their fearsome appearance. They live in rock cracks and caves and are widespread in Africa. Leg span up to 120 mm.

Pseudoscorpions (Order Pseudoscorpiones). These tiny arachnids measure less than 8 mm and look like miniature tailless scorpions. They have venom glands in their pedipalps and silk glands in their chelicerae. They create silken chambers in which they overwinter, moult and raise their young. Some species are cosmopolitan, using birds and other animals for transport. Widespread in Africa.

Ricinuleids (Order Ricinulei). Ricinuleids are small (5-10 mm), lethargic, beetle-like arachnids. They are found in leaf mould and other humid environments in tropical areas. Rarely seen and harmless, only about 25 species are known.

Solifuges (Order Solifugae). Solifuges or sun spiders are hairy, spider-like creatures which move very rapidly. They have a pair of enormous, forward-projecting chelicerae which are used to attack and chew their prey. The pedipalps are leg-like and serve as tactile organs. Solifuges are widespread in Africa, are harmless and range in size between 8 and 70 mm.

Harvestmen (Order Opiliones). Harvestmen are normally mistaken for spiders but, on close inspection, they can be distinguished by their longer, spined pedipalps, segmented abdomens and by the lack of a constriction between the abdomen and prosoma. Harvestmen are abundant in forests and have a leg span of up to 80 mm.

Ticks and mites (Order Acari). Ticks and mites belong to different suborders of the Acari. After the spiders, the Acari is the largest arachnid order, having over 20 000 species. All ticks are parasitic and range in size from 3-15 mm. They are important vectors of disease and are widespread. Mites range in size from 0,1-6 mm.

Spider suborders

Side view of a four-lunged spider's chelicera showing how the fang opens and closes parallel to the long axis of the body

4 lungs

Downward biting action of the four-lunged spider

Frontal view of a two-lunged spider's chelicerae showing how they open and close at right angles to the long axis of the body

2 lungs

Sideways biting action of the two-lunged spider

In Africa, two suborders of spiders are recognized, the Orthognatha (mygalomorphs) and the Labidognatha (araneomorphs). Most species of Orthognatha are large ground-dwellers and they are generally regarded as being primitive. These spiders are easily distinguished by the fact that their chelicerae open and close in a plane parallel to the long axis of the body. They have four lungs.

Species of the Labidognatha are normally small to medium-sized and have only two lungs. Some also have a tracheal tube which usually opens near the spinnerets. The chelicerae open and close in a plane at right angles to the long axis of the body. Most of the web-making spiders belong to this suborder.

Growth

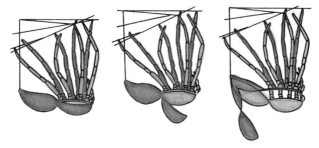

Stages of a spider moulting. The old skin splits from the front (near the eyes) and the spider gradually frees itself. The old skin is left suspended in the web

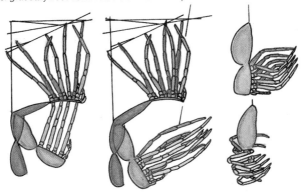

Spiders have a relatively inflexible exoskeleton, and for this reason the only way they can increase in size is to shed the old exoskeleton or 'skin' periodically. This process is termed moulting or ecdysis.

A young spider will stop feeding about a week before a moult is due. During this period, enzymes dissolve the inner layers of the old cuticle, while at the same time, secretory cells lay down a new cuticle beneath the old. When these processes have been completed, the old skin splits and is shed.

The cuticle of a freshly moulted spider is very soft, and the spider is thus extremely vulnerable at this stage. To expand its new skin, the spider sucks in air and it is after this that the new skin starts to harden. A spider can increase its size by about 20 per cent at each moult and most species undergo about eight moults before they reach maturity. Only fully mature spiders can mate with each other as the external sexual organs only appear during the final moult.

Field notes and species illustrations

Baboon spiders (family Theraphosidae:
genera *Harpactira, Ceratogyrus, Harpactirella, Pterinochilus*)

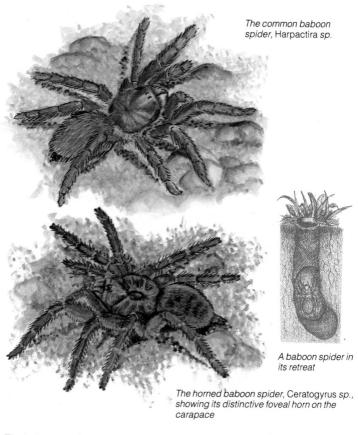

The common baboon spider, Harpactira *sp.*

A baboon spider in its retreat

The horned baboon spider, Ceratogyrus *sp.,*
showing its distinctive foveal horn on the carapace

The baboon and trap-door spiders are the best known representatives of the Orthognatha or four-lunged spiders in southern Africa. The baboon spiders are related to the so-called tarantulas or bird-eating spiders of the New World, which are much sought-after as pets. In recent years local baboon spiders have been sold as pets but, unlike their American counterparts, they are rarely successful as such. Unless young specimens are obtained and allowed to construct silk-lined burrows 30-40 cm deep (from which they

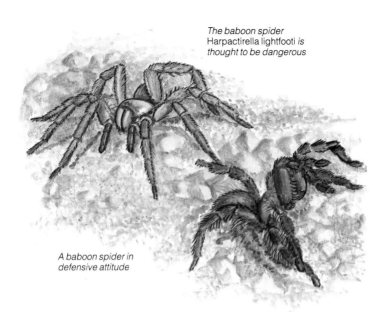

The baboon spider
*Harpactirella lightfooti is
thought to be dangerous*

A baboon spider in
defensive attitude

seldom emerge), they normally stop eating and die within two to three months.

In southern Africa the family Theraphosidae is represented by several genera such as *Harpactira*, *Harpactirella*, *Pterinochilus* and *Ceratogyrus*. Of these, only the latter is easily recognized by the non-specialist as it has a prominent foveal horn projecting from the centre of its carapace. Virtually all live in silk-lined burrows up to 40 cm deep. However, *Harpactirella*, which occurs on the islands off the Cape west coast, is often found under stones. One species, *Harpactirella lightfooti* is reputed to be dangerously venomous but there is no scientific evidence for this belief.

When alarmed or threatened, the baboon spider rears up with its front legs outstretched and from this position strikes downwards at its adversary or prey. This spider has very long poison fangs which can inflict nasty wounds. The venom is mildly toxic to man.

A theraphosid is easily identifiable by its large size (up to 12 cm across the legs), stout legs and small, raised dome which bears all its tiny eyes. In most species, the body is covered with hair-like setae that resemble the fur coat of a baboon or monkey. This explains the vernacular name.

☐ **Bobbejaanspinnekoppe.**

Section through the chelicera of a
baboon spider, showing the position of
the venom gland and the venom duct
leading to the tip of the fang

11

Trap-door spiders
(family Ctenizidae: genera *Stasimopus*, *Galeosoma*)

Stasimopus *sp.*

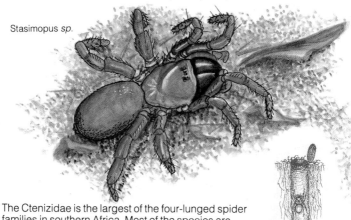

The Ctenizidae is the largest of the four-lunged spider families in southern Africa. Most of the species are medium to moderately large spiders and they live in silk-lined burrows 10-20 cm deep. Each burrow is equipped with a snug-fitting lid, the top of which is covered with soil. When closed, only the keenest observer can detect these burrows as they are extremely well camouflaged. The lid protects the spider from predators and from flooding when it rains. At night the spider half opens the trap door and lies in wait at the burrow entrance for prey to crawl by.

Species of the genus *Galeosoma* are readily distinguishable because of their truncated abdomens. The posterior surface of the abdomen is protected by a circular armoured plate, the diameter of which approximates that of the burrow. The spider is thus able to seal off the burrow at any point to reduce the chances of predation.

Trap-door spiders normally have short, stout, shiny legs and their bodies are not very 'hairy'.
□ **Valdeurspinnekoppe.**

Galeosoma *sp. seals off the burrow with its armoured abdomen*

View of Galeosoma *sp. showing the circular armoured plate which is used to seal off its burrow from potential predators*

Sac spiders
(family Clubionidae: genus *Chiracanthium*)

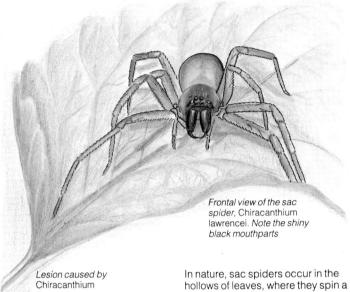

Frontal view of the sac spider, Chiracanthium lawrencei. *Note the shiny black mouthparts*

Lesion caused by Chiracanthium

The long chelicerae and eye pattern of Chiracanthium sp.

In nature, sac spiders occur in the hollows of leaves, where they spin a few strands of silk to form a sac — hence their name. However, they are equally at home in the corners of doors and walls and in the folds of curtains and clothes. At night they leave their temporary daytime retreats and forage as free-ranging hunters. These spiders are distinguished by their quick movements and aggressive behaviour, their straw-coloured bodies and huge, shiny black chelicerae. The eyes are arranged in two parallel rows of four.

Sac spiders often bite sleeping people or those who get dressed in clothes that harbour the spiders. Characteristically two bite marks 6-8 mm apart are visible. A bite from a sac spider causes an inflamed swollen lesion that ulcerates after a few days. ☐ **Sakspinnekoppe.**

13

Widow spiders
(family Theridiidae) 💀

Black widow spider *Latrodectus indistinctus* (formerly *L. mactans*)

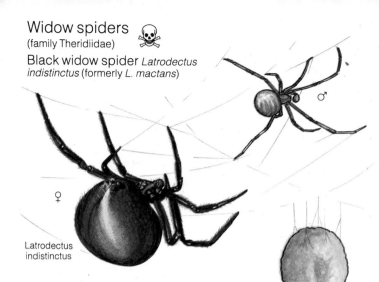

♂

♀

Latrodectus
indistinctus

egg case

abdominal markings

Black widow spiders are probably the most feared of all spiders. The local species is called the button spider. Although legend has it that the female eats her partner after mating and thus becomes a widow, there is little evidence to support this belief.

Black widow spiders are widespread and generally found among rocks in long grass. Local species can be recognized by body shape and red markings. Young females have an obvious red stripe or stripes down the upper side of the abdomen. These stripes are usually reduced with each successive moult until an old female merely has a dull red dot above her spinnerets. Some specimens may also have small white or yellow spots dorsally on the abdomen. Males are similar but much smaller. Local species have no ventral markings, unlike those from other parts of the world. The smooth egg cases are about 10 mm in diameter and are commonly found in the female's messy web. Females feed on beetles and occasionally may even ensnare small vertebrates.

In man, the bite is extremely painful and gives rise to alarming symptoms but is rarely fatal. Very few local deaths have been recorded. The venom acts on nerve endings. An antivenom is produced by the S.A. Institute for Medical Research in Johannesburg. □ **Swart knopiespinnekop**.

Distribution in Africa

Brown widow spider
Latrodectus geometricus

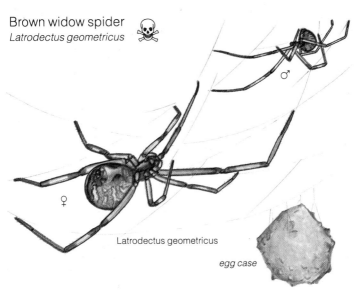

Latrodectus geometricus

egg case

The brown widow or hourglass spider is a cosmopolitan species which is abundant in southern Africa. It is most commonly found within city areas where it makes its messy cobwebs under window-sills, behind gutters, in the cavities and corners of walls and so on. The webs often contain several egg cases and these are of diagnostic value: they are spiked whitish balls about 8 mm in diameter. The brown widow varies tremendously in colour, ranging from pitch black through brown and cream to a bluish-grey. All the colour forms have a characteristic orange hourglass-shaped marking on the underside of the abdomen, and some specimens also have intricate and beautifully coloured markings on the top of the abdomen. The leg joints show dark bands. The male, which is very small and lacks the hourglass marking, is often found in the female's nest.

Many people misidentify the brown widow as a black widow: while closely related to the black widow, *L. geometricus* is not regarded as being of medical importance although its bite may be very painful. □ **Bruin knopiespinnekop**.

Some of the colour variations of L. geometricus

Violin spiders
(family Loxoscelidae: genus *Loxosceles*)

Ecologically, the violin spiders can be divided into two groups, namely the cave and the savanna species. The cave species are normally a dark brownish black with black markings and have small eyes, while savanna species are either golden yellow or light brown with black markings and have relatively large eyes. Most loxoscelines are delicate spiders with bodies 8-10 mm in length and a leg span of 50 mm. Violin spiders have only six eyes – most spiders have eight. □ **Vioolspinnekoppe**.

Loxosceles parrami

Loxosceles parrami

This species is known only from the Witwatersrand where it is widespread. It is a cave dweller which has been artificially introduced by man into the urban environment. It is found in the dark nooks and crannies of many buildings, or under floors. These spiders can be identified by their dark brown colour and the transverse boomerang-shaped black markings on the abdomen.

At night the spiders roam about in search of food such as fishmoths. During these wanderings they may come into contact with humans or become entangled in clothing; over 70 per cent of human bites occur at night while

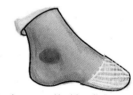
Lesion caused by bite of L. parrami

Distribution of L. parrami *in the Transvaal*

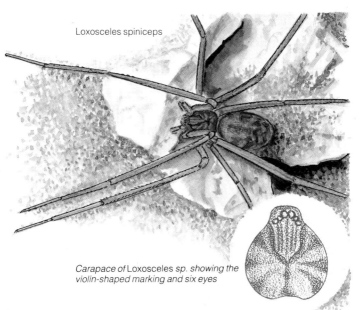

Loxosceles spiniceps

Carapace of Loxosceles *sp. showing the violin-shaped marking and six eyes*

the victim is asleep. There is no pain at the time of biting and it may take several hours before any symptoms appear. Initially the lesions are characterized by severe inflammation and swelling. The affected tissues die and slough off in about a week, leaving an ulcerating lesion which can take many weeks to heal. These lesions may measure up to 10 cm across. *L. parrami* is responsible for most cases of violin spider bite in southern Africa.

Loxosceles spiniceps *and related species*

L. spiniceps is typical of the savanna species and is widespread in the Transvaal, Zululand and Zimbabwe. It has a golden body with a black chevron pattern on the abdomen. The violin-shaped marking is clearly visible. Savanna species live beneath rocks or logs or in small abandoned burrows and, because of their cryptic coloration, they are often difficult to see. Females construct silk-lined hemispherical depressions in the sand in which they lay their eggs. About 15 eggs are deposited in these egg cases and then covered with sand.

Bites by these spiders are rare and clinically they are similar to those of *L. parrami.*

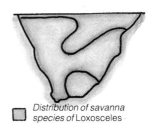

Distribution of savanna species of Loxosceles

Six-eyed crab spiders
(family Sicariidae: genus *Sicarius*)

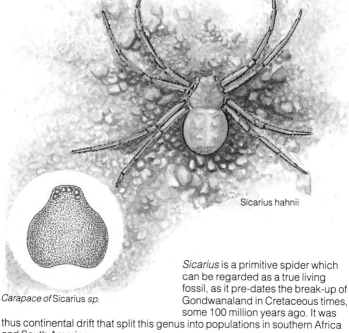

Sicarius hahnii

Carapace of Sicarius *sp.*

Sicarius is a primitive spider which can be regarded as a true living fossil, as it pre-dates the break-up of Gondwanaland in Cretaceous times, some 100 million years ago. It was thus continental drift that split this genus into populations in southern Africa and South America.

Sicarius, which is closely related to the violin and spitting spiders, is also called the self-burying spider because it uses its front legs to kick sand over its body until it is completely submerged. Normal habitats are beneath rocks or buried in the sand at the entrances of small animal burrows, at the bases of rock overhangs, or in caves. These spiders are found in arid and semi-arid areas with six species occurring in the Cape and Namibia and one, the largest species *S. oweni*, in the northern Transvaal.

They are medium-sized spiders with a body length up to 15 mm, and the width across the legs 50 mm. Most species are reddish brown to yellow but these colours are rarely seen as the spider

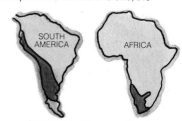

Distribution of the genus Sicarius

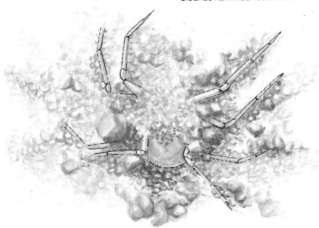

effectively camouflages itself with sand particles wedged between the body setae. In this way it takes on the exact colour and texture of its environment. *Sicarius* may be identified by its self-burying behaviour, its six very small eyes and tough, leatherlike body which is dorso-ventrally compressed. It does not spin a web and spends most of its life motionless, buried in sand.

Prey is caught when it crawls over the buried spider. The spider leaps out of the sand, grasps the prey with its front legs and bites it. A well-fed spider can easily survive a year or more without food or water: under laboratory conditions they eat only three or four times a year. These spiders take a long time to develop and may live for up to 15 years.

All southern African sicariids have very toxic venoms, the most dangerous species being *S. hahnii* which occurs in the north-western Cape northwards into Namibia. This is almost certainly one of the world's most dangerously venomous spiders. Fortunately they are not aggressive and bite only under duress. In addition, their habitats and behaviour limit the possibility of human contact under normal circumstances. The venom causes massive tissue destruction at the bite site and serious internal bleeding. The victim's lungs, liver and heart are affected within hours of a bite. It is not known how many people have been bitten by these spiders: a few suspected cases have involved loss of limbs and one death has been reported. No antivenom is available at present and you should thus avoid handling these spiders at all costs. □ **Sesoog-krapspinnekoppe**.

Spitting spiders
(family Scytodidae: genus *Scytodes*)

A female Scytodes fusca *carrying her egg case in her mouth. The egg case is carried until the spiderlings hatch*

In southern Africa, two species are commonly found in houses: the cosmopolitan *Scytodes thoracica* which is yellowish with black markings and *S. fusca* which is black. Morphologically these spiders are very similar to *Loxosceles* with which they are frequently confused. Like *Loxosceles*, they have six eyes, and are small, delicate spiders with long, slender legs. The only feature which distinguishes them from *Loxosceles* is the shape of the carapace which slopes upwards from the front to form a slight hump at the back. They are free-ranging and do not construct webs.

To capture their prey, these spiders spit a thick, sticky secretion at their victim and literally stick it to the substrate. The secretion is produced in the venom glands and is squirted out through the two tiny chelicerae. Once the prey is stuck to the substrate, the spider starts feeding.

Scytodes species should be welcomed in the home for they are totally harmless to man and serve him well by preying almost exclusively on fishmoths. □ **Spoegspinnekoppe.**

Feather-legged spiders
(family Uloboridae: genus *Uloborus*)

Uloborids sit near the centre of their webs. The characteristic posture which makes them difficult to identify as spiders is shown: the hind legs are drawn close to the body and the long, stout front legs are held together and outstretched

At first sight this tiny spider in its beautiful orb web is unlikely to attract much attention. Although the orb webs of the uloborids closely resemble those of the araneids (p. 35), these families are not at all closely related. One often finds their small horizontal webs among rocks and they are also found close to the webs of other spiders such as *Cyrtophora*. However, they sometimes enter buildings, especially garden sheds.

The spiders are small, roughly 5 mm across the legs, and variously coloured. They sit at the centre of their webs with their hind legs drawn close to the body. The longer front legs are outstretched and held together. Possibly the most interesting feature of these spiders is the fact that they are the only spiders which do not have venom glands. Their prey is trapped in the web, then encased with silk and eaten alive. Uloborids are cribellate spiders (p. 31). □ **Veerpootspinnekoppe**.

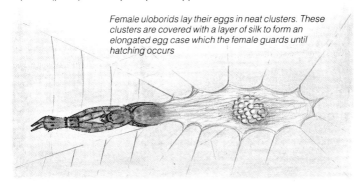

Female uloborids lay their eggs in neat clusters. These clusters are covered with a layer of silk to form an elongated egg case which the female guards until hatching occurs

Nursery web spiders
(family Pisauridae: genera
Thalassius, Euphrosthenops)

Nursery web spiders are members of a diverse group which includes the fishing spiders. Most pisaurids are medium-sized to large spiders and are easily distinguished by the prominent and characteristic white bands which run down the edge of the carapace and abdomen on each side.

The illustration above shows Thalassius spenceri *drifting on the water surface. The spider relies on the surface tension of water and the non-wettable wax covering of its body in order to remain afloat. If the water is polluted with detergent or soap, which reduce surface tension and act as wetting agents, the spider will sink immediately. (Below) Female pisaurids carry their egg cases in their mouths until they are almost ready to hatch*

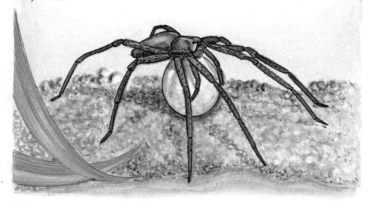

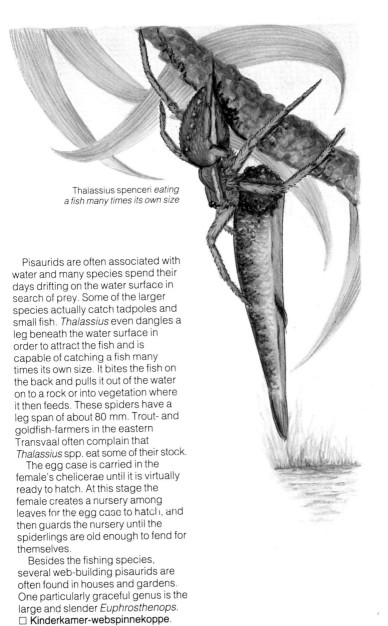

Thalassius spenceri *eating a fish many times its own size*

Pisaurids are often associated with water and many species spend their days drifting on the water surface in search of prey. Some of the larger species actually catch tadpoles and small fish. *Thalassius* even dangles a leg beneath the water surface in order to attract the fish and is capable of catching a fish many times its own size. It bites the fish on the back and pulls it out of the water on to a rock or into vegetation where it then feeds. These spiders have a leg span of about 80 mm. Trout- and goldfish-farmers in the eastern Transvaal often complain that *Thalassius* spp. eat some of their stock.

The egg case is carried in the female's chelicerae until it is virtually ready to hatch. At this stage the female creates a nursery among leaves for the egg case to hatch, and then guards the nursery until the spiderlings are old enough to fend for themselves.

Besides the fishing species, several web-building pisaurids are often found in houses and gardens. One particularly graceful genus is the large and slender *Euphrosthenops*. ☐ **Kinderkamer-webspinnekoppe.**

23

Wandering or Lizard-eating spider
(family Sparassidae: *Palystes natalius*)

A female Palystes natalius *stalking a small lizard*

Most sparassids are large, free-ranging spiders which do not construct conventional webs. The most common species in the Pretoria/Johannesburg city area is the *Palystes natalius*. It often rests, legs outstretched, on walls at night, and many people feeling their way in the dark have inadvertently touched these huge, fast-moving and aggressive spiders. The experience is rarely forgotten! However fearsome these spiders may appear, they are in fact harmless.

Palystes natalius is called the lizard-eating spider because it generally preys on small lizards and geckos. Because of their large size (body length 25 mm and leg span 90 mm), *Palystes* species are often mistaken for the baboon spiders. They are distinguished by the sideways biting action of their chelicerae, two lungs, and yellow and black ventral banding on the legs.

Formerly, it was believed that these spiders were dangerously venomous because, in laboratory tests, guinea pigs they bit died within about three minutes. However, it was recently demonstrated that the guinea pigs died of shock and that the venom is harmless. □ **Grootdwaalspinnekop; Akkedisvreter.**

P. natalius *in defensive posture*

White lady
(family Sparassidae:
genera *Leucorchestris*, *Carparachne*)

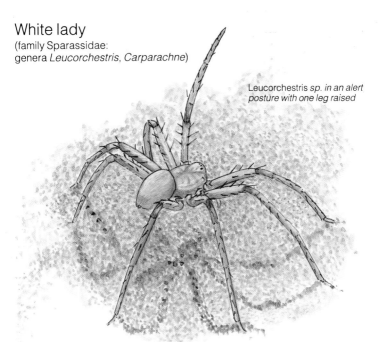

Leucorchestris *sp. in an alert
posture with one leg raised*

The white lady is large white sparassid restricted to the sand-dune
areas of the Namib desert. When disturbed, these spiders display
strange behaviour: they jump up and down in a frenzied, dance-like
fashion. They also have an unusual escape mechanism in that, if
threatened, they cartwheel at great speed down the slip-face of a
sand-dune.

It is very difficult for the novice to distinguish between
Leucorchestris and *Carparachne* which also occurs in the Namib, but
Leucorchestris is larger and may exceed 100 mm across the legs.
□ **Wit dame**.

Leucorchestris *spp. have a unique way of avoiding
trouble — they curl up and roll down the sand-dune*

Wolf spiders
(family Lycosidae:
genera *Lycosa*, *Pardosa*,
Hippasa, etc)

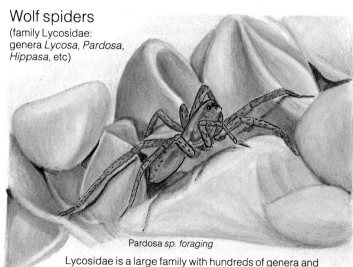

Pardosa sp. foraging

Lycosidae is a large family with hundreds of genera and thousands of species world-wide. Generally, lycosids are fast-moving, free-ranging hunting spiders with good vision. They run down their prey in a wolf-like manner, hence their common name. Lycosids inhabit a wide range of habitats such as beneath stones, under bark, in fallen trees, in compost heaps and in grass. Lycosids are the most common spiders in lawns and other ground covers and one sees them in great numbers when they are disturbed as lawns are mowed. Most species are greyish or brownish with dark markings and they range in size from a few millimetres to several centimetres across the legs. The eye pattern is the best distinguishing feature: the eyes are arranged in three rows, two in each of the upper rows and four in the bottom row. The two large eyes in the central row are diagnostic.

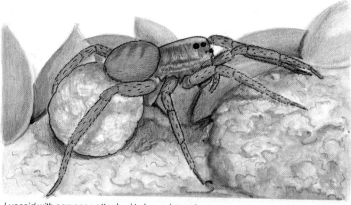

Lycosid with egg case attached to her spinnerets

Lycosid with young on her back

The female carries the egg case attached to her spinnerets. In many species, the young climb on to the mother's back and spend up to two weeks there after hatching, in much the same way as scorpions do.

Many of the European species which live alongside the banks and shores of rivers and lakes navigate by the sun and stars. This was proved by placing spiders in planetariums and rotating the positions of the stars while monitoring the orientation of the spiders. It is quite possible that certain southern African species also use astral cues.

Wasps often lay their eggs in lycosids. They sting the spider to paralyse it before depositing the egg. The larva hatches and parasitizes the spider which remains paralysed but alive for the entire development period of the larva. This process may take several days and in some cases may exceed a week, after which the emaciated spider dies. □ **Wolfspinnekoppe**.

Lycosid parasitized by a wasp larva

Jumping spiders
(family Salticidae: genus *Myrmarachne*, etc.)

Male salticids are generally more attractive than females of the same species. Their hairy pedipalps and front legs are often eye-catching and are used for the complicated semaphore signalling system these spiders have evolved

Most jumping spiders are less than 5 mm in length and not easily seen which is a pity as they are among the most attractive and interesting spiders. A great many species exist and the family is the largest in the order. Jumping spiders stalk their prey until they are within range and then leap at the prey in much the same way as a lion would at an antelope. Before each leap, the spider attaches a silk thread to the substrate so that it can climb back in the event of a misjudged jump.

Although these spiders are such active jumpers, they do not have muscles in their legs capable of providing motive power. Instead, the energy is derived from a sudden increase of blood pressure in the legs. This causes the legs to straighten and this in turn 'kicks' the spider into the air.

Salticids can be recognized as they have a pair of huge eyes at the front of the carapace. The eyes have large retinas which give the spiders very keen eyesight. They can detect the slightest movement and accurately judge the position of their prey prior to leaping at it in attack. The acute eyesight plays an important role in the courtship of many species. When a male sees a female, he starts a semaphore-like signalling with his front legs. A responsive female will signal back and mating will ensue. The

Frontal view of a salticid's face

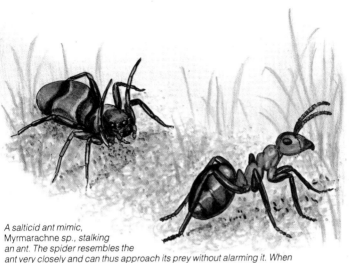

A salticid ant mimic,
*Myrmarachne sp., stalking
an ant. The spider resembles the
ant very closely and can thus approach its prey without alarming it. When
in range, the spider leaps at the ant and kills it by injecting it with venom*

semaphore codes are species specific. Males and females are
approximately the same size but the males are generally more brightly and
beautifully marked.

The males of many salticid species are aggressive to possible
competitors of the same species. If another male is encountered, the
semaphore signalling is initiated and this may be followed by a mock battle
in which the dominant male chases off the submissive male. Try placing a
small mirror in front of one of these spiders and then watch the
communication between the spider and his image, followed by attempted
battle with the image.

Because salticids are so dependent on vision for foraging and
reproduction, they are almost exclusively diurnal. At night they retreat into
cracks and crevices and seal themselves in little silken cocoons for security.
The female also lays her eggs in a cocoon which she then guards until the
spiderlings have hatched and can fend for themselves.

Several salticid genera contain species that mimic ants, the best-known in
Africa being *Myrmarachne*. Species of this genus look just like the ant
species which they mimic. As a spider has eight legs and an ant six, this
spider's front legs are not used for walking but are waved about in the air in
the same way the ants use their antennae. The spider walks on the last three
pairs of legs. The body is elongated and in some species may be
constricted which gives the impression of three body regions. Even the body
markings are similar to those of the ants and many an entomologist has been
fooled by these cunning impostors. They are generally found in the vicinity of
the ant nests of the species they mimic and prey on; some species even

A tiny salticid in a typical posture prior to jumping. The eyes assess the size and distance of the prey. Salticids have the best-developed eyes of all spiders

walk in line with the ants on their trails. Besides being able to prey on the ants, the spiders are also protected by them from other predators, as the individual spiders are 'diluted' in the crowd of ants. Males of the *Myrmarachne* generally have large, forward-projecting chelicerae.

It takes time to learn to recognize these mimics but it is time well spent as you will be well rewarded by being able to watch them in action. Look for them on trees on which ants occur, or near ant nests.

Over the years, salticids have been implicated in a few spider bite cases. These bites have resulted in neurotoxic-type envenomations. Thus far, laboratory studies have failed to substantiate the claims and it would appear that most if not all species are harmless. However, one should always treat a salticid with respect, no matter how mildly toxic it is thought to be.
☐ **Springspinnekoppe**.

A male salticid engaged in semaphore signalling. Both the front leg pairs and the pedipalps are used in the complex signalling systems of these spiders. Signalling takes place when a male encounters another male or a receptive female

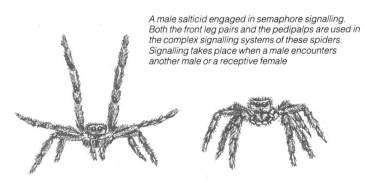

Velvet spiders (family Eresidae: genera *Seothyra*, *Stegodyphus*, *Gandanameno*, *Magunia*, etc.)

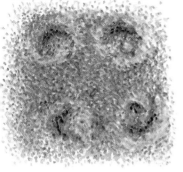

The surface appearance of a Seothyra *web in sand. The actual web is buried in the sand and all one can see from above are the four corners of the web. The indentations caused by the four corners where they attach to the surface give rise to a hoofprint-like image in the sand*

These are small to medium-sized, robustly proportioned spiders which have 'flat' faces. The eresids, together with the uloborids (p. 21) and a few other minor families not represented in this book, are termed cribellate spiders because they have a cribellum: a perforated plate-like structure in front of the spinnerets which produces hackled threads. Seen under a microscope, these threads have a frayed, woolly appearance, but even to the

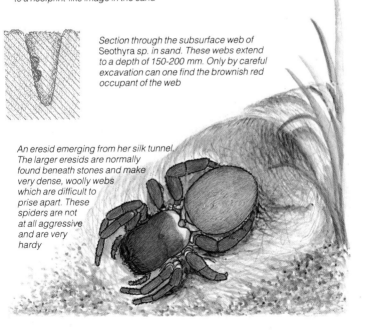

Section through the subsurface web of Seothyra *sp. in sand. These webs extend to a depth of 150-200 mm. Only by careful excavation can one find the brownish red occupant of the web*

An eresid emerging from her silk tunnel. The larger eresids are normally found beneath stones and make very dense, woolly webs which are difficult to prise apart. These spiders are not at all aggressive and are very hardy

31

naked eye they seem soft and diffuse in comparison with silk threads produced by other spiders. Cribellate spiders have a row of short, spine-like setae on their hind legs and use these combs to draw out the silk from the cribellum. The hackled threads are used to entangle prey.

Eresids are a very varied group of spiders which range from exotically coloured, solitary species to social species. Except for the social spiders, most eresids are associated with soil. They live beneath stones or under bark, near the base of trees. The strangest member of the family is probably *Seothyra* which creates a tube-like web in soft sand. All one can see on the surface are the four corners which are 6-8 cm apart. The surface of the web resembles a hoof-print, and few people seeing this print would realize that it was a spider web. The females and young remain in the webs but the males are surface feeders, preying on certain ant species which they mimic. These spiders occur in the sandy areas of the northern Transvaal and arid areas of the western half of southern Africa.

Nest of a social spider, Stegodyphus *sp., made between the strands of a barbed wire fence. Normally these webs are made in acacia trees. The webs are easily seen against the light in the early morning or late afternoon*

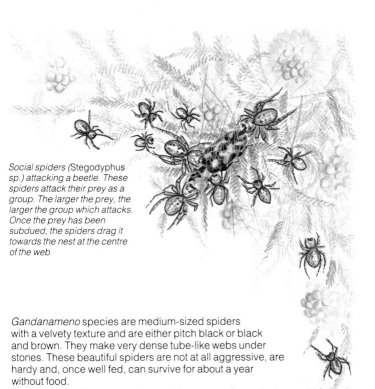

*Social spiders (*Stegodyphus sp.*) attacking a beetle. These spiders attack their prey as a group. The larger the prey, the larger the group which attacks. Once the prey has been subdued, the spiders drag it towards the nest at the centre of the web*

Gandanameno species are medium-sized spiders with a velvety texture and are either pitch black or black and brown. They make very dense tube-like webs under stones. These beautiful spiders are not at all aggressive, are hardy and, once well fed, can survive for about a year without food.

Social spiders. The social spiders of the genera *Stegodyphus* and *Magunia* are well known. A colony of these spiders creates a compact, messy labyrinthian nest in a thorn tree or along a wire fence. Silk snares radiate in sheet-like fashion from the nest. When an insect flies into the snares, a great many of the spiders leave the nest and attack the unfortunate intruder *en masse*. The subdued prey is dragged up to the nest area of the web for hungry members of the colony to share. Social spiders will respond to any sustained movement at a given point in their web. Thus they will respond to the low-frequency struggling movements of a beetle and also to the high-frequency wing movements of a trapped fly. Movement caused by wind does not activate the spiders.

These little spiders can easily be studied in your home: simply remove the branch on which a colony of the spiders is established and hang it in your study or kitchen. It will serve as an efficient fly trap and the spiders will continue to live normally provided they get enough food. When a colony gets too large, some members leave in pairs to start new colonies.

☐ Fluweelspinnekoppe.

Daddy-long-legs

(family Pholcidae:
Pholcus and *Smeringopus* spp.)

Pholcids, like scytodids and pisaurids, carry their egg cases in their mouths until they begin to hatch. Shown here is a female Pholcus *sp. with her egg case*

Most people take these harmless spiders for granted because they are such a familiar sight: the daddy-long-legs is easily recognized by virtue of its elongated cylindrical abdomen, its exceptionally long, slender legs and its web.

These spiders make their loose, untidy webs in the darker corners of houses and garages and, in nature, they construct their webs among rocks or in caves. One species, *Pholcus phalangioides*, the long-bodied cellar spider, is cosmopolitan. Some species have only six eyes.

Females carry their egg cases in their mouthparts until the spiderlings hatch. When threatened or when prey lands in their web, pholcids vibrate vigorously, shaking the web to ensure that anything resting on it becomes entangled and trapped. □ **Langbeenspinnekoppe**.

Face of Pholcus *sp. showing the tiny chelicerae*

Carapace of Pholcus *sp. showing the eye pattern*

Orb-web weavers
(families Araneidae, Nephilidae
and Tetragnathidae)

The orb-web weavers consist of many closely related families which are generally characterized by the webs they spin.

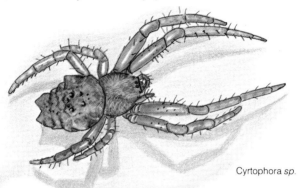

Cyrtophora *sp.*

Dome-web spiders (family Araneidae: genus *Cyrtophora*)

Species of *Cyrtophora* are very common in gardens and often annoy gardeners by constructing their webs among prized plants. The spider is not spectacular and most species are either grey or brown to black with white markings. Six prominent dorso-lateral lobes are the main features of the abdomen.

The web of this spider is interesting in that it is a very intricate, near perfect lace-like horizontal construction. Strong vertical threads support the web and act as knock-down strands: when an insect flies into one or more of these strands, it generally falls on to the horizontal lace section, below which the spider waits. Before the insect can escape, the spider rushes out beneath it and attacks. Egg cases are elongated oval structures which are attached to the web in such a way that they look like debris. □ **Koepelwebspinnekoppe**.

Cyrtophora *suspended in her web*

Golden orb-web weavers
(family Nephilidae: genus *Nephila*)

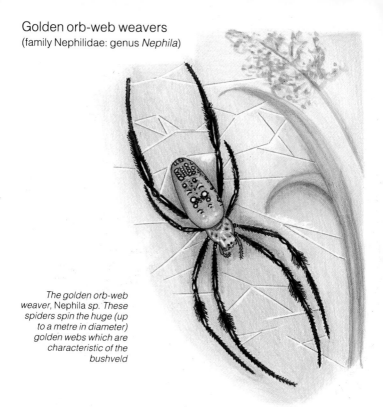

The golden orb-web weaver, Nephila sp. These spiders spin the huge (up to a metre in diameter) golden webs which are characteristic of the bushveld

These huge (body 35 mm, leg span 80 mm) but delicately proportioned spiders are easily recognized by their cylindrical, intricately patterned abdomens, and banded legs, often with dense tufts of hairs near the articulation points. All the species spin golden threads and their huge orb webs, up to a metre in diameter, are a common sight among the thorn trees of the bushveld. The webs are very strong and occasionally ensnare small birds.

Three species occur in southern Africa and these can be recognized by their colour patterns which are species specific. Males are very small and inconspicuous and have a body mass roughly one thousandth that of the female. □ **Gouewawielwebspinnekoppe.**

Garden orb-weavers
(family Araneidae: genus *Argiope*)

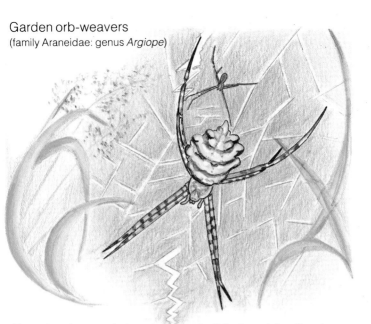

The garden orb-weaver, Argiope *sp., in her web with the tiny male in waiting above. When she is busy eating, the male will mate with her. Below the female, the stabilimentum, which is composed of zig-zag threads, can be seen*

Species of the genus *Argiope* are usually large and spectacular, silver and yellow spiders with black markings. Females of some species are large (body 25 mm and 80 mm leg span), have lobed or ribbed abdomens and spin huge, perfect orb webs up to 75 cm across. Males are small and plain in comparison with the females.

The male, attracted to the female's web by pheromones, takes up a position a few centimetres above the female. When the female captures prey and starts feeding on it, the male climbs down on to her abdomen and mates with her. As soon as the female stops feeding, the male leaves her and takes refuge in the upper reaches of the web. The mating process is repeated many times over a period of three or four days.

An interesting feature of the web is a belt of zig-zag threads which radiates from the hub of the web and which is known as a stabilimentum.

☐ **Tuinwawielwebspinnekoppe**.

*A female kite spider,
Gasteracantha sp. By
contrast, the males are
plain and small*

Kite spiders
(family Araneidae: genus *Gasteracantha*)

Perhaps no spider genus is as easily recognized by the layman as
Gasteracantha. The abdomen of this attractive spider is flat and hard and
terminates in a number of sharp horns, laterally and posteriorly. The armed
abdominal shields are beautifully coloured red, yellow or white with bright,
contrasting markings. *Gasteracantha* is always much wider than it is long but
rarely exceeds 10 mm in length. The males are even smaller and are very plain.
   The orb webs of these spiders are characteristically found in forest areas.
The female rests at the hub of the web. □ **Vlieërspinnekoppe**.

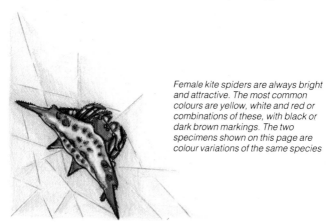

*Female kite spiders are always bright
and attractive. The most common
colours are yellow, white and red or
combinations of these, with black or
dark brown markings. The two
specimens shown on this page are
colour variations of the same species*

Bark spiders
(family Araneidae: genus *Caerostris*)

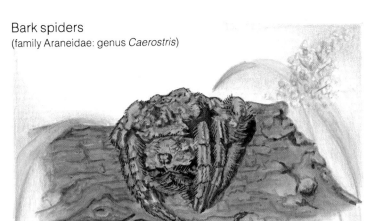

A bark spider, Caerostris *sp., camouflaged on a branch*

Bark spiders are medium-sized spiders which construct orb webs at night. When day approaches, they dismantle or abandon the webs and rest on the small branches of thorn trees. These spiders are so perfectly camouflaged that they resemble nodules on the branch and people rarely see them. Rows of setae down the sides of their legs break up any contrasting lines which might reveal them to predators. Some species have two thorn-like processes on the abdomen. Forest species are diurnal and do not dismantle their webs. The leg span of bark spiders ranges between 25 and 35 mm.
☐ **Basspinnekoppe**.

Long-jawed water spiders
(family Tetragnathidae: genus *Tetragnatha*)

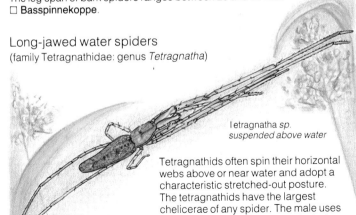

Tetragnatha sp.
suspended above water

Tetragnathids often spin their horizontal webs above or near water and adopt a characteristic stretched-out posture. The tetragnathids have the largest chelicerae of any spider. The male uses his chelicerae to hold the female during mating. ☐ **Grootkaakwaterspinnekoppe**.

39

Bolas spiders (family Araneidae: genus *Cladomelea*)

A female Cladomelea akermani in her web swinging the bolas with which she catches her prey. Several egg cases can also be seen in the web

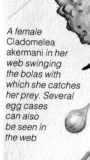

Cladomelea akermani is a medium-sized spider (body length 15 mm) which constructs a nest by using silk threads to bind a few blades of grass into a bundle. The crude nest is not easily seen unless it houses several of the large egg cases (15 mm across) which the female attaches to the shafts of the grass bundle.

These spiders have a cunning hunting behaviour. Shortly after dark the female *Cladomelea* spins a horizontal thread to which she attaches a small ball of a thick, sticky secretion. The thread is cut and the ball allowed to hang just above the ground. The female grasps the other end of the thread with her third leg and swings it in a circular path. (Related spiders in America and Australia use one of their first legs to swing the bolas.) The swinging sticky ball will adhere to any insect that it strikes and the spider then simply pulls the prey up to her nest. Because the ball loses its stickiness as it dries, the spider replaces it approximately every fifteen minutes with a fresh ball and eats the old one. Some scientists believe that the sticky ball contains a substance similar to that found in the female moth's sex attractant which draws males from considerable distances. It has been noted that bolas spiders catch mainly male moths. □ **Bola-spinnekoppe.**

Crab spiders
(family Thomisidae)

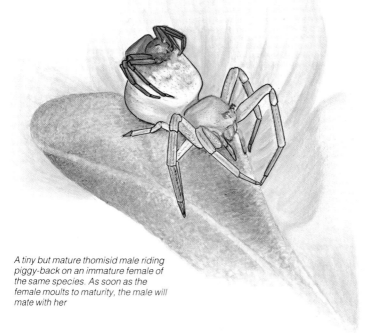

A tiny but mature thomisid male riding piggy-back on an immature female of the same species. As soon as the female moults to maturity, the male will mate with her

Crab spiders derive their name from their crab-like appearance and movements: they can walk sideways, forwards or backwards as the need arises. They are normally found on plants and especially flowers where their bright colours camouflage them as they sit with their front legs outstretched. Any insect attracted to the flowers may fall prey to these spiders. Most of the local species have a leg span of less than 15 mm.

One species observed has an interesting mating behaviour. The mature male, which is a fraction the size of the female, selects a subadult female partner and rides piggy-back on her, waiting for her to reach maturity. To reach maturity, the female has to moult and when this happens, the new skin is very soft and takes several hours to harden (p. 9). Spiders are virtually defenceless during this critical hardening period.

When the female starts moulting, the male climbs off her and waits for her to emerge from her old skin. As soon as she does and while she is still soft and defenceless, the male mates with her. About a month after the mating, the female lays eggs and seals these in a silken sac that she guards until the spiderlings hatch. □ **Krapspinnekoppe**.

Funnel weavers

(family Agelenidae: genera *Agelena*,
Tegenaria)

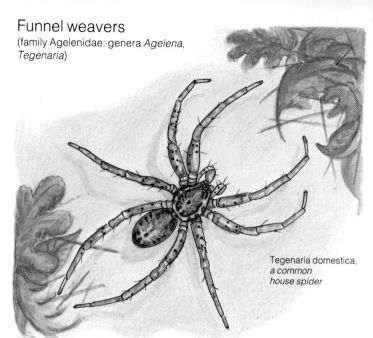

Tegenaria domestica,
a common
house spider

Although funnel weavers are very common spiders they are shy and humans seldom see them. They are, nevertheless, easily recognized by their very long spinnerets, wolf-spider-like appearance and small cluster of eight tiny eyes. Two species are abundant in southern Africa, namely *Agelena australis* outdoors and the cosmopolitan *Tegenaria domestica* indoors.

Their funnel web consists of a tubular retreat which opens out to form a horizontal sheet web 30-40 cm across. The retreat tube is generally made beneath rocks or in holes in walls, etc. The sheet region of the web is normally constructed over grass and when an insect walks over it, the vibrations attract the spider which rushes out of its retreat to attack the trespasser. The prey is dragged into the retreat region of the web and eaten.

Females lay their disc-shaped egg cases in the retreat regions and often die before their young hatch. ☐ **Tregterwebspinnekoppe**.

Funnel web of
Agelena australis

42

Lynx spiders
(family Oxyopidae: genera
Oxyopes, *Peucetia*)

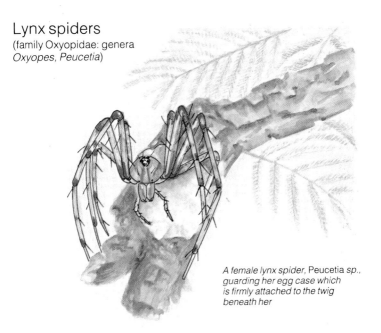

A female lynx spider, Peucetia *sp.,
guarding her egg case which
is firmly attached to the twig
beneath her*

Oxyopids are hunting spiders and are called lynx spiders because of their cat-like behaviour of jumping at flying insects and chasing their prey over vegetation. All the species are associated with plant habitats.

Several pallid species of *Oxyopes* occur in southern Africa but the green lynx, *Peucetia* sp., is spectacularly beautiful. It has a semi-transparent green body with red and black markings. Characteristic of the family are the domed frontal region of the carapace, the abdomen tapering posteriorly and the groups of long black spines evenly distributed over the legs. *Oxyopes* species are small to medium in size whereas *Peucetia* species have leg spans of up to 50 mm.

Most species attach their egg cases firmly to small branches or leaves. Females guard their egg cases until the spiderlings hatch.

☐ **Tierspinnekoppe**.

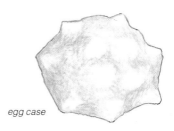

egg case

Armoured spiders
(family Zodariidae)

These spiders can be distinguished by the fact that their front spinnerets are considerably longer than the hind pair. Most zodariids are medium to large spiders, with a leg span of more than 10 mm.

The illustrations show the various stages in which the clumsy Caesetius deserticola *inverts while burrowing into the sand*

One species, *Caesetius deserticola*, is common on the dunes of the Namib desert. This sand-coloured spider can bury itself in the sand within seconds by using its front legs to burrow, and it virtually 'swims' through the sand. As it burrows, it gradually inverts so that when it comes to rest buried just below the surface, it is upside-down with its legs and fangs facing any possible prey that might walk over it. When on the surface, *C. deserticola* appears to be very clumsy.
□ **Pantserspinnekoppe**.

Ogre-faced spiders

(family Dinopidae:
Dinopis and *Menneus* spp.)

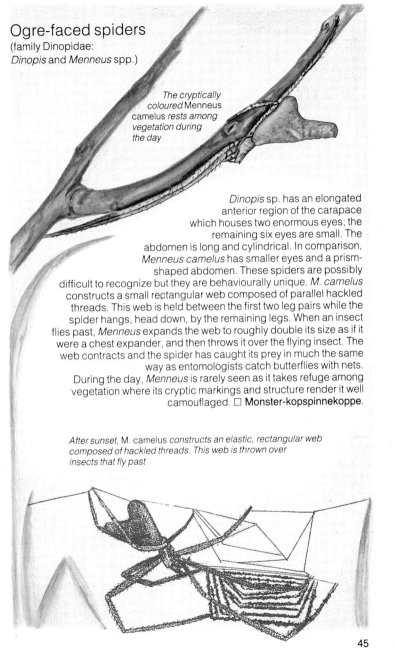

The cryptically coloured Menneus camelus *rests among vegetation during the day*

Dinopis sp. has an elongated anterior region of the carapace which houses two enormous eyes; the remaining six eyes are small. The abdomen is long and cylindrical. In comparison, *Menneus camelus* has smaller eyes and a prism-shaped abdomen. These spiders are possibly difficult to recognize but they are behaviourally unique. *M. camelus* constructs a small rectangular web composed of parallel hackled threads. This web is held between the first two leg pairs while the spider hangs, head down, by the remaining legs. When an insect flies past, *Menneus* expands the web to roughly double its size as if it were a chest expander, and then throws it over the flying insect. The web contracts and the spider has caught its prey in much the same way as entomologists catch butterflies with nets. During the day, *Menneus* is rarely seen as it takes refuge among vegetation where its cryptic markings and structure render it well camouflaged. ☐ **Monster-kopspinnekoppe**.

After sunset, M. camelus *constructs an elastic, rectangular web composed of hackled threads. This web is thrown over insects that fly past*

Intertidal spiders
(families Amaurobioididae,
Desidae, Hahniidae and
Linyphiidae)

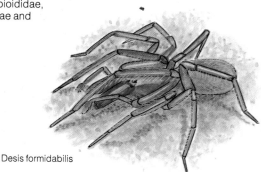

Desis formidabilis

Although the intertidal spiders of southern Africa belong to different families,
it is convenient to treat them as a separate entity on ecological and
physiological grounds. Four species from four families inhabit the intertidal
zones of southern Africa, namely *Desis formidabilis* (Desidae) and
Muizenbergia abrahami (Hahniidae), *Amaurobioides africanus*
(Amaurobioididae) and *Erigonopsis littoralis* (Linyphiidae). All these spiders
spend their entire lives on the rocks between the low and high tide water
levels and thus during the periods of high tide are totally submerged in sea
water.

During low tide, the intertidal species behave as 'normal' spiders and
spend the time searching for food. However, when the tide starts coming in,
they move to their retreats and spin silk threads over the entrances to help
resist wave action. Intertidal spiders usually choose the empty shells of
molluscs wedged between the rocks as retreats to protect them from high
tide.

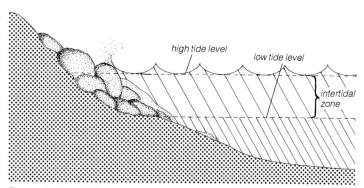

*The area between the high and low tide levels is known as the intertidal zone and it is
here that the spiders live*

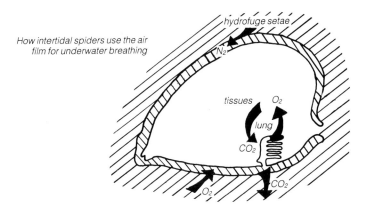

How intertidal spiders use the air film for underwater breathing

They have evolved special physiological adaptations to enable them to cope with total immersion in sea water each day. Like many aquatic insects, the abdomens of these spiders are covered with a dense packing of wax-coated hairs called hydrofuge setae. When the spider is submerged, the surface tension of the water leads to the creation of a film of air between the spider's body and the tips of the hydrofuge setae, which imparts a silvery appearance to the spider. Because the spider's lungs open into this trapped air film, its oxygen can be consumed. As carbon dioxide is water soluble, it is dissolved as fast as it is exhaled. The nitrogen in the film serves to maintain the gas volume of the film but as oxygen is consumed, the gas balance is disturbed. To compensate and restore the balance, oxygen dissolved in the sea water is released into the film. Therefore, provided there is nitrogen in the film, the spider will be able to get sufficient oxygen to last the duration of the high tide.

Spiderlings live with their mothers in silk-lined shells until they are old enough to fend for themselves. □ **Tussengety-spinnekoppe**.

Female Amaurobioides africanus *with young in shell*

Cannibalistic spiders
(families Mimetidae and Gnaphosidae)

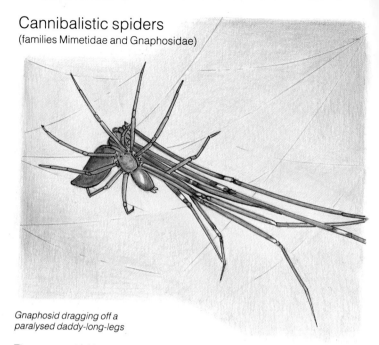

*Gnaphosid dragging off a
paralysed daddy-long-legs*

There are probably many spiders that prey on other spiders from time to
time, but not many specialize in attacking other species in their webs. At
least one gnaphosid species attacks the daddy-long-legs (p. 34) in its web.
Pirate spiders (family Mimetidae) are regarded as the villains of the spider
world. Mimetids sneak into the webs of other spiders such as araneids
(p. 35) and bite the occupants. Their venom contains a muscle relaxant that
paralyses the occupant of the web which is then dragged off and devoured.
One species is possibly even more cunning in that it mimics the courtship
behaviour of the male araneid trying to enter the female's web. When the
female responds to the web plucking, she is attacked.
 Behaviour aside, pirate spiders are identified by their yellowish bodies
with black markings, egg-shaped carapace, long, slender chelicerae, and a
row of stout, curved setae on the tarsi of the first legs.
 Females suspend their egg cases from vegetation and leave them
unattended. □ **Roofspinnekoppe**.

Webs

Webs are constructed to form a custom-made habitat for the spider, and thus make it less dependent on environmental conditions. Webs are species specific and there are as many different methods of construction as there are web types.

Stages in the construction of a web
To construct an orb web, a bridge is made. Normally the spider releases a thread into the wind until it touches and adheres to another surface. This bridges the gap. After this, the radii are formed and, finally, the spiral is made.

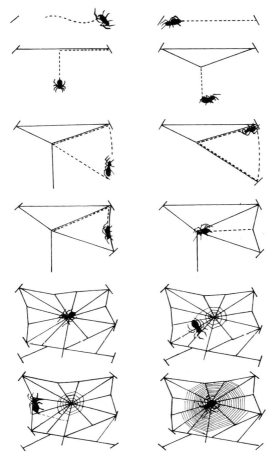

Webs of the *Uloborids*

Radial web of *Hyptiotes* sp., the triangle spider

The triangle spider makes its simple but distinctive
web among rocks or vegetation. The tiny spider rests
on the single strand that leaves the apex of the
triangular region. Hackled threads are laid down
in the segments of the triangle.

Orb-like web of *Uloborus* sp.

These orb-like webs resemble those of the Araneidae but differ in that the
spiral threads are of hackled silk, not sticky strands.

Orb web of *Argiope* sp.

Orb webs of *Argiope* and
other members of the
Araneidae range from
medium to very large
spiral webs, and they
are what most people
envisage when they
think of spider webs.

Hammock web of a
linyphiid spider

Linyphiidae is one of the larger spider families, yet these spiders are so small
and drab that they normally go unnoticed. However, early in the morning
after a heavy dew their tiny sheet or hammock webs can be clearly seen on
most lawns.

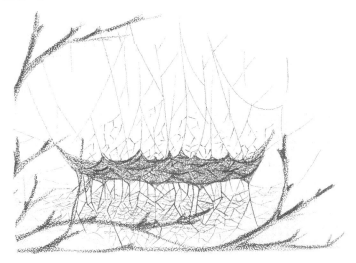

Horizontal sheet or dome web of *Cyrtophora* sp.

The horizontal sheet region of these webs consists of a very delicate lace-like structure which is normally iridescent in sunlight. The sheet region is anchored by numerous vertical strands which serve to knock down insects flying past. The insect falls on to the sheet region, beneath which *Cyrtophora* sp. waits.

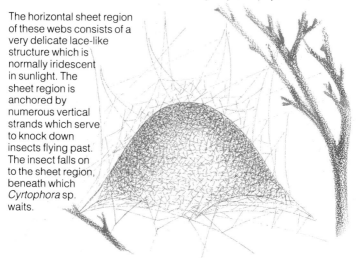

Funnel web of *Agelena australis*

The funnel webs of *Agelena* are a common feature in highveld vegetation. They are normally seen in grass surrounding derelict buildings or among rocks. The spider spends the day in the tubular retreat region of the web and waits for prey to land on the sheet region which extends outwards from the retreat.

Where spiders live

Forest habitat

Argiopidae
Clubionidae
Thomisidae
Sparassidae

Eresidae   *Pisauridae*
Salticidae   *Clubionidae*
Argiopidae   *Thomisidae*
Oxyopidae

Argiopidae
Thomisidae
Salticidae
Lycosidae
Theraphosidae

Savanna & bushveld habitat

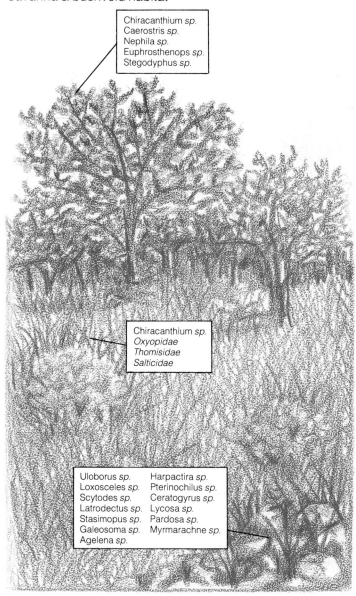

Chiracanthium *sp.*
Caerostris *sp.*
Nephila *sp.*
Euphrosthenops *sp.*
Stegodyphus *sp.*

Chiracanthium *sp.*
Oxyopidae
Thomisidae
Salticidae

Uloborus *sp.*	Harpactira *sp.*
Loxosceles *sp.*	Pterinochilus *sp.*
Scytodes *sp.*	Ceratogyrus *sp.*
Latrodectus *sp.*	Lycosa *sp.*
Stasimopus *sp.*	Pardosa *sp.*
Galeosoma *sp.*	Myrmarachne *sp.*
Agelena *sp.*	

Desert habitat

Leucorchestris *sp.*
Carparachne *sp.*
Caesetius *sp.*

Sicarius *sp.*
Loxosceles *sp.*
Latrodectus *sp.*

Seothyra *sp.*

Reproduction

Courtship

There are probably as many courtship and other behavioural patterns associated with the reproductive process as there are spider species. These behaviour patterns are very interesting and intricate and it is a great pity that so few of them have been recorded. This is a field of study in which the amateur with very little equipment can excel.

Courtship and mating behaviour function to bring two members of the same species but of the opposite gender together for the purposes of reproduction. The importance of these functions can be gauged by the fact that a species has been defined as 'a group of animals that share a specific-mate recognition system'. Some spiders such as the salticids have elaborate courtships involving semaphore-like communications between potential partners. The pedipalps and legs are used for these sophisticated signals and good vision plays an important role, although the more primitive spiders such as *Sicarius* and *Loxosceles* spp. have poor vision. When a male encounters a female he will stridulate (make a faint sound) and then gently touch the female with outstretched front legs to assess her receptiveness. Some female spiders give off pheromones which act as sex attractants. The male follows the wind-borne scent trail to the female's web. Males of certain species pluck the threads of the female's web in order to test her mood and disposition towards them.

Receptive partners will mate. In order to fertilize the female, the male inserts his sperm-filled palpal embolus into the female epigynum. The structure of the male and female organs is such that they fit into each other precisely. Each species has its own uniquely shaped genitalia and these function as a type of lock and key mechanism. Many biologists believe that

Mating

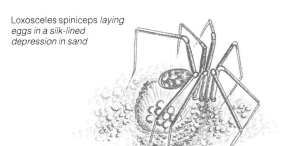

Loxosceles spiniceps *laying eggs in a silk-lined depression in sand*

these mechanisms prevent different species from mating with each other. Because the structure of spider genitalia is so species specific, biologists use these organs to classify and identify species. When a new species is described, illustrations of the male and female structures are always provided.

The female stores the sperm until it is needed to fertilize eggs. Fertilized eggs are laid in silken egg cases and a female can produce a number of egg cases over a period of several weeks following a single mating. The number of eggs in a case varies according to species and can range from half a dozen to several hundred.

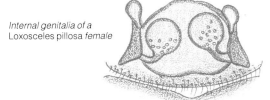

Internal genitalia of a Loxosceles pillosa *female*

Most spiders do not care for their young in any way and the newly hatched spiderlings have to fend for themselves from birth. However, lycosids do care for their young during their second instar. The young climb on to the mother's back and remain there for up to two weeks, after which they moult and leave home.

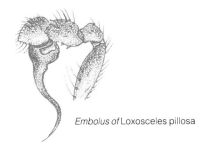

Embolus of Loxosceles pillosa

Aerial dispersal

Many spiders are capable of aerial dispersal from their place of birth by a process called ballooning. After hatching, the spiderling climbs to an elevated position in its environment, such as up a blade of grass or a pole. When a gentle breeze blows, the spiderling faces the wind and, abdomen curved upwards, it releases a strand of silk. When the strand is long enough (10-30 cm depending on its size) the spiderling releases its hold on the substrate and lifts off into the wind, suspended by its silk thread.

The silk strands on which the spiders 'balloon' are called gossamer threads and they have been known to carry the spiders hundreds of kilometres over land and sea: ballooning spiders have been captured at altitudes of up to 4 500 metres. Small wonder therefore that spiders are normally among the first land animals to inhabit newly-formed volcanic islands. The best-known balloonists are theriids (widow spiders) of the genus *Latrodectus*, and linyphiids (hammock weavers) of the genera *Lepthyphantes* and *Erigone*.

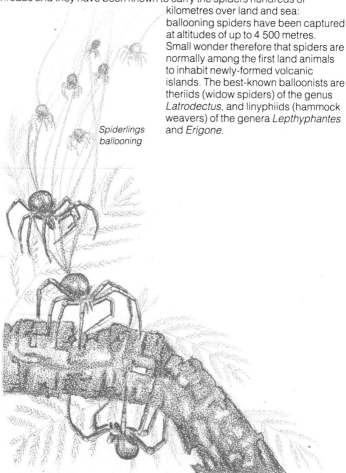

Spiderlings ballooning

Collecting spiders

Spiders are very delicate creatures and easily damaged during the process of capture. Never grasp a spider by one of its legs as it will almost certainly separate from the body. The best way to capture a spider is to coax it into a jam jar by gently prodding it with a pencil or twig. Never pick up a spider by hand! If a spider does have to be handled, do so with great care, using delicate watchmaker's forceps or soft entomological forceps, and always grip the spider by the body.

Spiders can be collected in various ways, such as by sweeping grass and other vegetation with a butterfly net, or by using a household sieve to sift dune spiders out of the sand in which they are buried. Non-web-bound hunting spiders can be trapped by burying an empty can or smooth-sided plastic container flush with the ground. A cover should be positioned one or two centimetres above the can to protect trapped spiders from the sun. Spiders are trapped when they fall into the can while running about in search of food. Some biologists half-fill these cans with 70% ethanol or ethylene glycol which kills and preserves the specimens.

Many spiders can be found beneath stones and other objects, under bark or in sea shells wedged in rock crevices in the intertidal zone.

Keeping spiders

The most effective way to kill spiders for a collection is to place them in the freezer compartment of a refrigerator for at least 20 minutes. Dead spiders are best fixed and preserved in a 70% solution of ethyl alcohol. The spider should be placed in a small glass tube fitted with a cotton wool plug which is then submerged in a glass jar containing 70% alcohol. Each specimen should have a label (filled out in pencil or Indian ink) which lists the name of the species, date and place of capture and other details.

A live spider can be kept in a variety of containers ranging from a jam jar to a terrarium, depending on the ecological needs of the spider. You should always try to satisfy the spider's natural needs. A web-bound species can be kept in a wooden frame covered with plastic sheeting taped in position with masking tape. The size of the spider's web in nature should give you an idea of the size requirements for the frame. A small hole can be made in the plastic sheeting through which insects can be pushed. When not in use, this hole can be sealed with masking tape. Once the spider has made a web and started feeding in the web, the plastic 'windows' can be removed. These frame containers are ideal for studying the web-building process.

Spider bites and their treatment

Very few of the 30 000 spider species known are potentially harmful to man. In southern Africa, four genera contain medically important species, namely *Latrodectus*, *Loxosceles*, *Chiracanthium* and *Sicarius*. Based on their action, spider venoms can be classified as either neurotoxic or cytotoxic.

The neurotoxic group: This group is represented by the black widow or button spider, *Latrodectus indistinctus*. Although greatly feared as deadly, the chances of death from the bite of this spider are extremely remote. However, the bite results in alarming and painful systemic signs and symptoms which may include generalized cramp-like pains, tightness across the chest, nausea, vomiting, difficulty in breathing and abdominal rigidity. It is important to calm the patient who is likely to be restless and shocked. Ice packs should be applied to the bite site as soon as possible and medical help should be sought. If possible, a tight crêpe bandage should be wound over the whole affected limb to immobilize it and thereby restrict the lymphatic system. The specific *Latrodectus* antivenom prepared by the South African Institute for Medical Research in Johannesburg is very effective and gives immediate relief. A calcium gluconate injection will give temporary relief. In any event, these medications should only be administered by qualified medical personnel.

The cytotoxic group: Local cytotoxic species belong to the genera *Chiracanthium*, *Loxosceles* and *Sicarius*. Normally pain only develops several hours after the bite, which is rarely felt. Signs and symptoms of cytotoxic spider bite start as either an inflamed or haemorrhagic lesion which may swell. In subsequent days the dead tissues slough, leaving an ulcerating wound anything up to 10 cm across. These wounds can take a long time to heal and it is thus important to prevent secondary bacterial and fungal infections. A doctor will prescribe the necessary antibiotics. No antivenom is available for the effective treatment of cytotoxic spider bite.

    The bites of *Chiracanthium* and *Loxosceles* spp. only cause local lesions whereas the bite of *Sicarius* is likely to cause serious complications involving internal bleeding. Fortunately, bites by *Sicarius* are extremely rare.

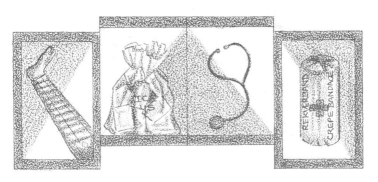

Glossary

Abdomen: The hind body region of a spider.

Carapace: The dorsal shield which covers the prosoma.

Chelicerae: Paired appendages on the head of the spider used for biting, chewing and grasping.

Cribellum: A perforated, plate-like spinning organ situated in front of the spinnerets of certain spiders (which are known as cribellate species).

Digestive caeca: Glandular pouches leading off the digestive tract which serve to store nutrients.

Diurnal: Active during the day.

Embolus: A duct which leads off the seminal bulb of male spiders' genitalia.

Epigynum: A cuticular process in front of the opening of the female genitalia.

Fovea: A pit or depression near the centre of the carapace.

Foveal horn: Instead of a fovea, some baboon spiders have a horn-like projection.

Hackled threads: Woolly threads spun by cribellate spiders and which serve to entangle prey.

Hydrofuge setae: Wax-coated setae which cover the body of aquatic spiders and other invertebrates. As the setae do not become wet, the spider is able to submerge in water with a thin film of air trapped among the hydrofuge setae. This can then be used as a source of oxygen.

Instar: The stage in development between any two moults.

Nocturnal: Active during the night.

Palps (or pedipalps): The second pair of appendages on the prosoma. In males they bear the external genitalia.

Pheromone: A substance which acts as a chemical signal among individuals of the same species. Pheromones play an important role as sex attractants in spiders.

Prebuccal cavity: The space in front of the mouth where digestion of food takes place before it is sucked through the spider's mouth.

Setae: Bristles and hair-like coverings of invertebrates.

Sexual dimorphism: Any structural differences between males and females of the same species. In general, male spiders are smaller, more slender and paler than females.

Spinnerets: External spinning organs near the rear of the abdomen.

Spiracle: The pore through which a spider breathes.

Stabilimentum: A band of denser silk in the webs of certain orb-web spiders. The purpose is not fully understood but it may serve as a camouflaging device.

Substrate: Soil or rock surface over which a spider moves or on which it lives.

Further reading

Bristowe, W.S. 1971. *The World of Spiders*. Collins, London.
Kaston, B.J. 1972. *How to know the Spiders*. W.M.C. Brown Publishers, Dubuque.
Kullmann, E. and Stern, H. 1981. *Leben am seidenen Faden – Die rätselvolle Welt der Spinnen*. Kindler Verlag, Munich.
Lawrence, R.F. 1964. *A Conspectus of South African Spiders*. Science Bulletin 369, Dept. Agricultural Technical Services.
Levi, H.W. and Levi, L.R. 1968. *A Guide to Spiders and their kin*. Golden Press, New York.
Maretic, Z. and Lebez, D. 1979. *Araneism with special reference to Europe*. Nolit Publishing House, Belgrade.

INDEX